# A COMPLETE MATHS PROGI
## FOR PRIMARY SCHOOL

**Planet Maths**

Senior Infants

**Angela Curley**

FOLENS

**Author:** Angela Curley
**Editor:** Donna Garvin
**Design and Layout:** Liz White Designs
**Illustrators:** Helen Prole (Plum Pudding), Gary Blatchford
**Photographs:** Thinkstock

ISBN: 978-1-84741-779-4

**First published in 2011 by:** Folens Publishers,
Hibernian Industrial Estate, Greenhills Road, Tallaght, Dublin 24.
Produced in Ireland by Folens Publishers.

The paper used in this book is sourced from managed forests.

## Introduction for Parents and Teachers

Planet Maths has been developed by a team of experienced primary teachers and consultants in accordance with the aims and objectives of the revised Primary School Curriculum and the accompanying Teacher Guidelines. Curriculum Strands, Strand Units and Objectives are detailed throughout.

The series underpins the key areas of:

- use of concrete materials
- development and correct use of mathematical language
- real life problem solving
- cooperative group work
- oral maths
- estimation
- written computation
- integration with other subjects

Planet Maths is a creative new maths series that aims to provide students with challenging activities and enjoyable mathematical experiences to help them become confident mathematicians.

## Authors

Rita Coleman and Liam Gaynor (6th), Elaine Burke (5th), Liam Gaynor (4th), Sue-Anne Synnott (3rd), Michelle Hande and Veronica Ward (2nd), Proinsias Ó Conghaile and Elaine McCann (1st), Angela Curley (Senior Infants), Deirdre Whelan (Junior Infants)

# Contents

# Look for us...

Benny

Betsy

Look for us at the top of the page. We will help you do your work.

# Colour

**Colour the kites red. Colour the balloons blue.**

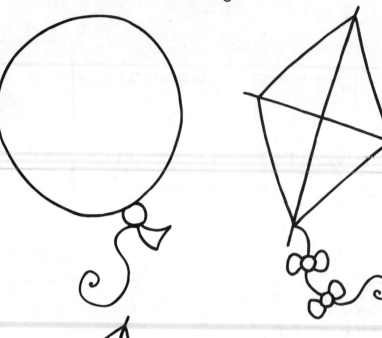

**Strand** Early Mathematical Activities
**Strand Unit** Classifying
Objectives Classify objects on the basis of colour.

**Colour Benny Bear and his balloons.**

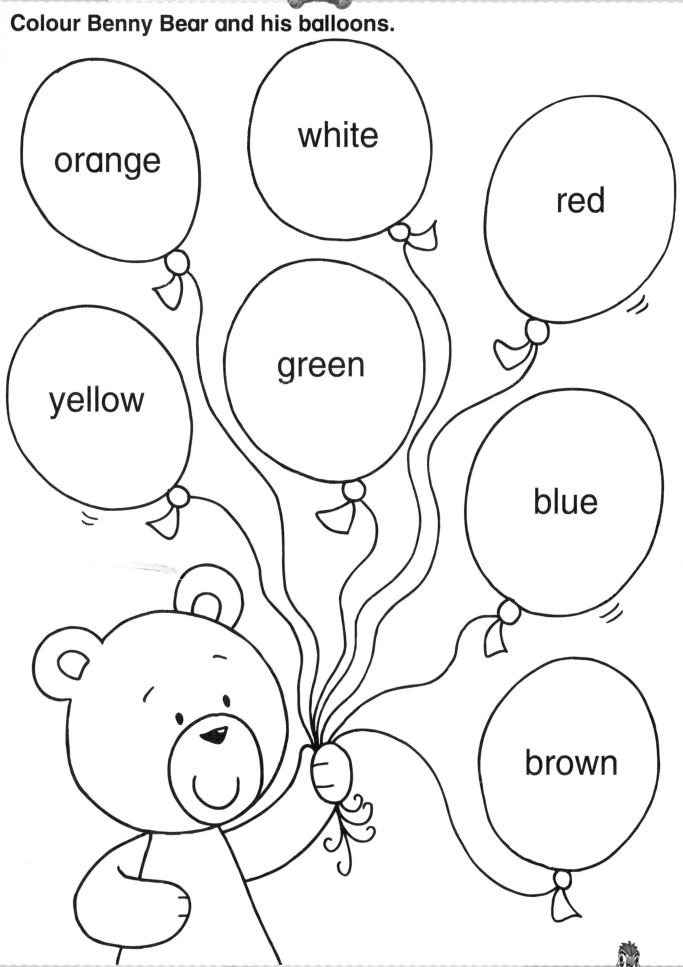

orange

white

red

yellow

green

blue

brown

| **Strand** | Early Mathematical Activities | Objectives | Classify objects on the basis of colour. |
| **Strand Unit** | Classifying | | |

7

# Match

**Match the pairs of bugs.**

          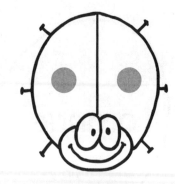

          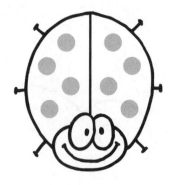

**Strand** Early Mathematical Activities

**Strand Unit** Matching

Objectives

Match pairs of identical objects in one-to-one correspondence.

## Match the pairs. Use the same colour for each pair.

**Strand** Early Mathematical Activities

**Strand Unit** Matching

Objectives Match pairs of identical objects in one-to-one correspondence.

q

# Sort

**Sort the objects into 3 sets.**

**Colour:** clothes   ● food   ● toys  ●

 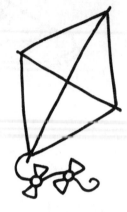 

| | | | Objectives |
|---|---|---|---|
| **Strand** | Early Mathematical Activities | | Sort a group of objects into three sets. |
| **Strand Unit** | Classifying | | |

# Sort

**Ring the one that is different in each row. Colour it red.**

| | |
|---|---|
| **Strand** | Early Mathematical Activities |
| **Strand Unit** | Classifying |

Objectives: Identifying the complement of a set ie. the odd one out.

11

# Numbers 1 and 2

## Draw the correct number of faces  in each box.

| 2 | 1 | 2 |
|---|---|---|

| 1 | 2 | 1 |
|---|---|---|

## Write the numerals.

| **Strand** | Number |
|---|---|
| **Strand Unit** | Counting |

**Objectives**
- Revision of counting up to 2.
- Writing numerals 1 and 2.

**Draw 1 spot ● on each dog. Draw 2 spots ● ● on each cat.**

## Write the numerals.

| Strand | Number |
|---|---|
| Strand Unit | Counting |

Objectives
• Revision of counting up to 2.
• Writing numerals 1 and 2.

**13**

# Number 3

Draw **3** lollipops for each bear. Use a different colour for each lollipop.

## Write the numeral.

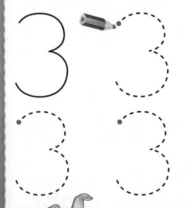     

14

| Strand | Number |
|---|---|
| Strand Unit | Counting |

Objectives
- Revision of counting up to 3.
- Writing the numeral 3.

## Draw 4 fish in the tank. Draw 4 spots on each fish.

## Write the numeral.

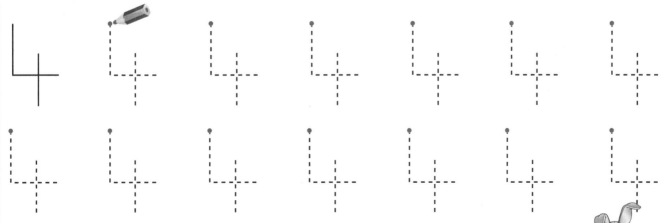

| Strand | Number |
| --- | --- |
| Strand Unit | Counting |

Objectives
• Revision of counting up to 4.
• Writing the numeral 4.

# Count

**Draw the correct number of spots on the children's t-shirts.**

3 green

1 yellow

2 red

4 blue

**Write the numerals.**

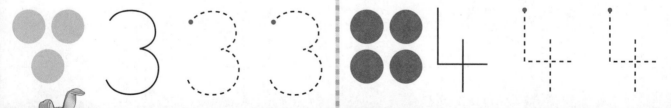

| Strand | Number |
|---|---|
| Strand Unit | Counting |

Objectives
• Revision of counting up to 4.
• Writing numerals 1–4.

**Draw 5 boats  on the sea.**

**Write the numeral.**

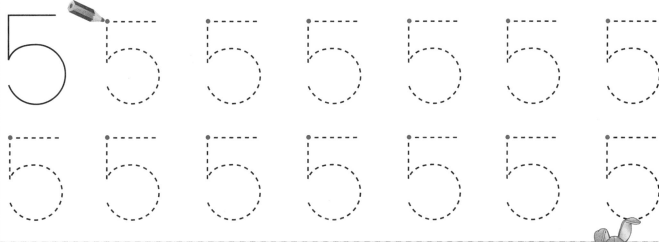

| Strand | Number |
| Strand Unit | Counting |

Objectives
- Revision of counting up to 5.
- Writing the numeral 5.

**17**

# Count

**Ring each set. Join each set to the correct numeral.**

| 1 |
|---|

| 5 |
|---|

| 2 |
|---|

| 4 |
|---|

| 5 |
|---|

| 3 |
|---|

| 2 |
|---|

| 3 |
|---|

**Strand** Number

**Strand Unit** Counting

Objectives Count the number of objects in a set totals to 5.

**Colour 2 spots red ●.**
**Colour 1 spot blue ●.**

 spots altogether

**Colour 3 spots green ●.**
**Colour 2 spots yellow ●.**

spots altogether

**Colour 1 spot orange ●.**
**Colour 1 spot purple ●.**

spots altogether

**Colour 2 spots black ●.**
**Colour 2 spots yellow ●.**

spots altogether

| Strand | Number | | Combine sets of objects totals to 5. |
|---|---|---|---|
| Strand Unit | Analysis of number | Objectives | |

 19

# Pattern

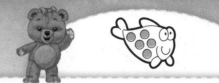

**Finish the pattern on each fish.**

**Strand** Algebra
**Strand Unit** Extending patterns
Objectives Identify, copy and extend pattern.

**Colour the kites to finish the pattern.**

# Number 6

Draw 6 lollipops  in the jar.

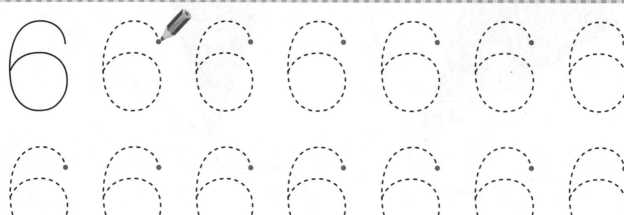

| Strand | Number |
| Strand Unit | Counting |

Objectives
• Counting up to 6.
• Writing the numeral 6.

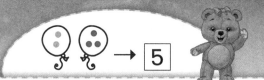

## Draw spots on Betsy's balloons. Count.

2    3    →    **How many?**    5

4    2    →    ☐

3    1    →    ☐

1    1    →    ☐

| Strand | Number | | |
|---|---|---|---|
| Strand Unit | Analysis of number | Objectives | Combining sets of objects totals to 6. |

# The Picnic

**Colour all the big bears purple. Colour all the little bears orange.**

## How many?

| | |
|---|---|
| **Strand** | Data |
| **Strand Unit** | Recognising and interpreting data |

Objectives — Count the number of objects in a set, totals to 6.

**Colour.**

 → green

 → brown

 → blue

 → orange

 → yellow

 → red

# Pattern

**Finish each pattern.**

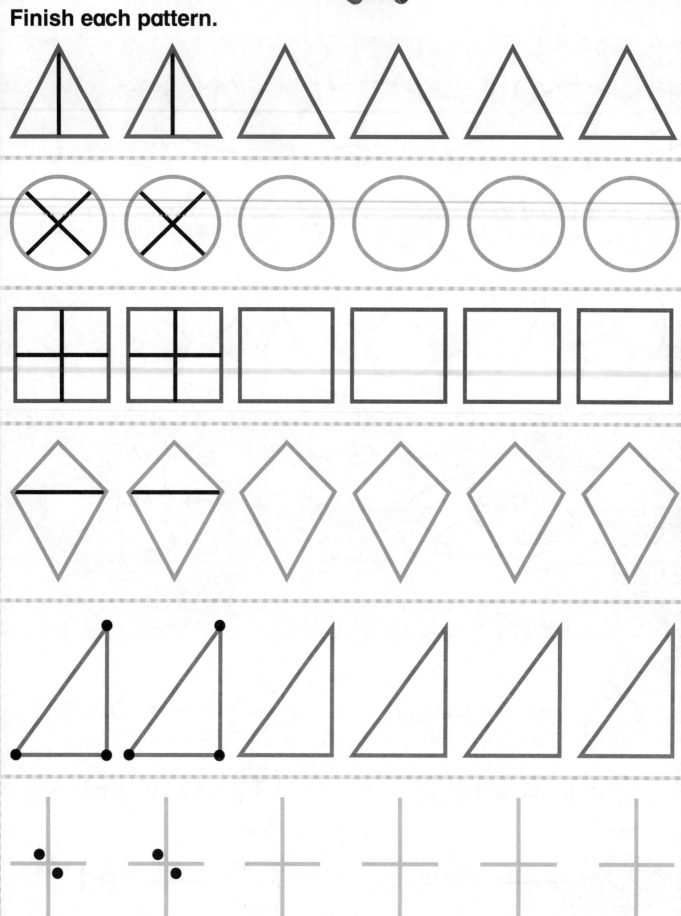

| **Strand** | Algebra | | Identify, copy and extend pattern. |
| **Strand Unit** | Extending Patterns | Objectives | |

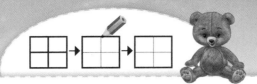

## Copy and repeat the pattern.

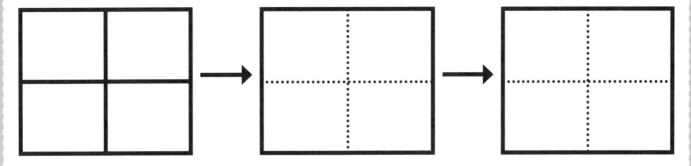

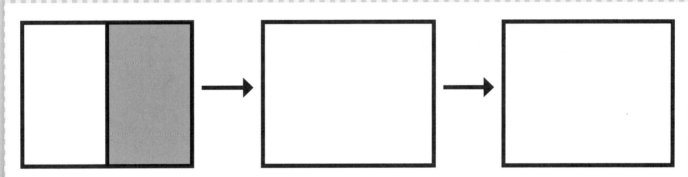

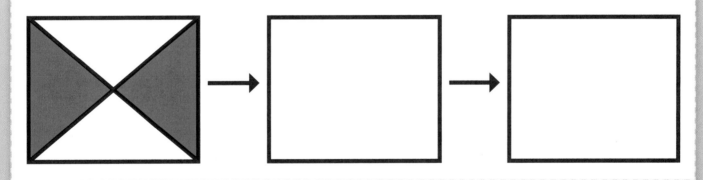

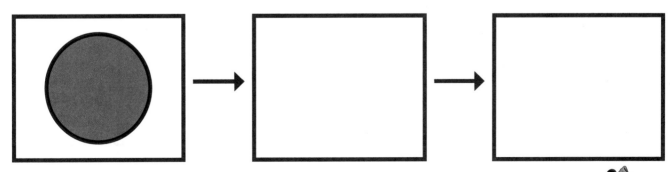

| Strand | Algebra |
|---|---|
| Strand Unit | Pattern |

Objectives Identify, copy and extend pattern

27

# Pattern

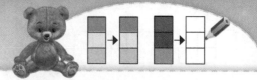

## Colour the boxes to match the patterns.

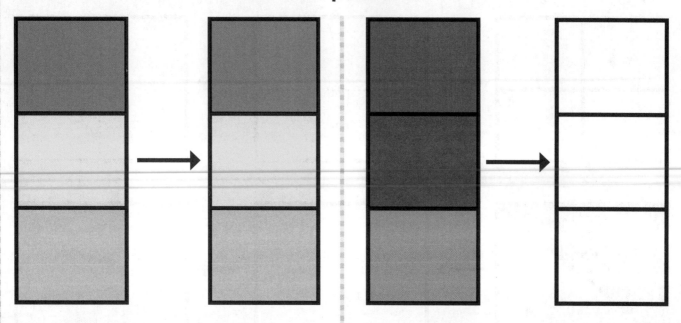

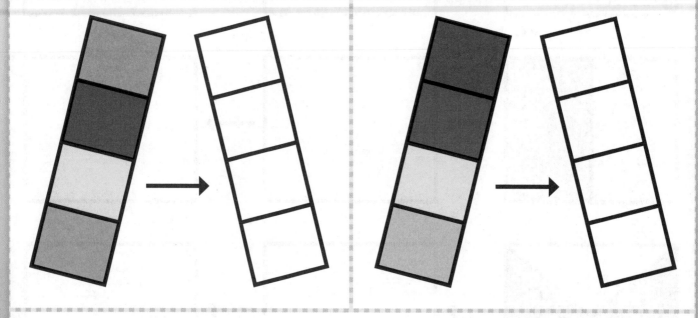

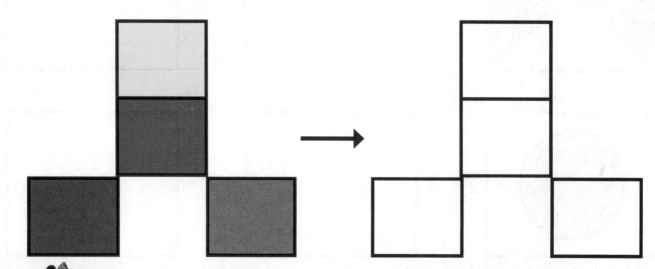

| Strand | Algebra |
|---|---|
| Strand Unit | Patterns |

Objectives | Identify and copy pattern.

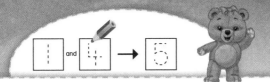

## Write the correct numerals.

1 and 4 → 5

5 and ☐ → ☐

☐ and ☐ → ☐

☐ and ☐ → ☐

☐ and ☐ → ☐

☐ and ☐ → ☐

☐ and ☐ → ☐

| Strand | Number |
|---|---|
| Strand Unit | Analysis of number |

Objectives: Combining sets of objects, totals to 6.

# Count

Benny Bear has found some shapes.

## square

## triangle

how many?

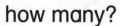

 sides

 corners

how many?

3 sides

corners

---

**Write.**

## square

## triangle

S _ _ _ _ _

t _ _ _ _ _ _

| Strand | Shapes and Space |
|---|---|
| Strand Unit | 2D shapes |

Objectives: Name and describe square and triangle, compare shapes and observe similarities and differences.

**Colour:** squares → ◼ triangles → ▲

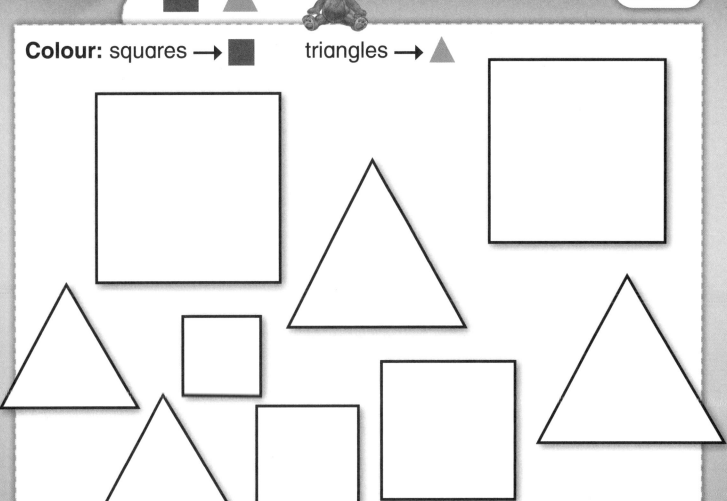

## How many?

 → _____      → _____

## Match the shapes. Colour each pair the same colour.

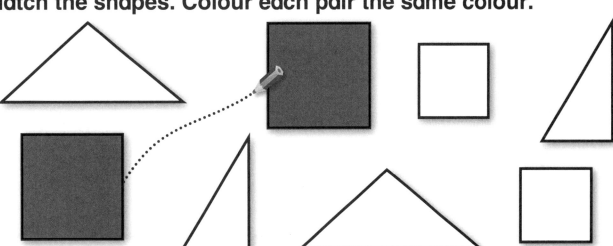

| **Strand** | Shapes and Space | Objectives | Sort and identify squares and triangles. |
| **Strand Unit** | 2D shapes | | |

31

Here are some more shapes.

## circle

## rectangle

how many?

 side

 corners

how many?

[ ] sides

[ ] corners

**Write.**

### circle

### rectangle

C _ _ _ _ _     r _ _ _ _ _ _ _ _

| Strand | Shape and Space |
| --- | --- |
| Strand Unit | 2D shapes |

Objectives: Name and describe circle and rectangle, compare shapes and observe similarities and differences.

**Colour:** circles ⟶ ● rectangles ⟶ ▭

---

**Draw 3 circles ◯.**

**Draw 2 rectangles ▭.**

**Strand** Shapes and Space
**Strand Unit** 2D shapes
Objectives  Identify and draw circles and rectangles.

**33**

# Draw

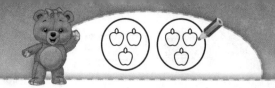

**Make the sets the same.**

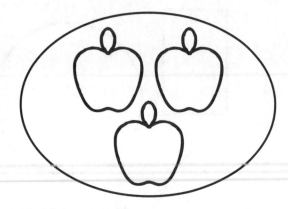 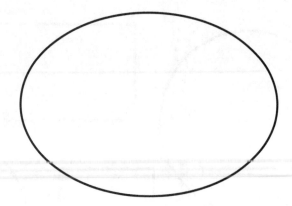

 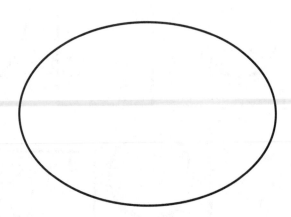

 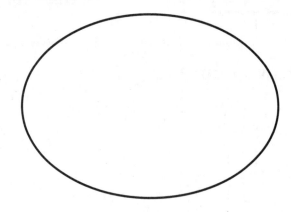

 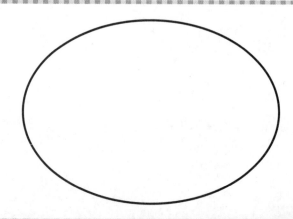

| Strand | Number |
| --- | --- |
| Strand Unit | Comparing |

Objectives    To explore the meaning of 'equal' or 'the same as'.

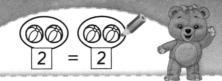

# Make the sets the same. Write the numerals.

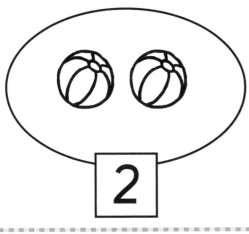

**2**

is the same as

**=**

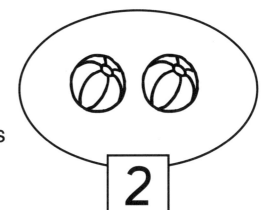

**2**

is the same as

**=**

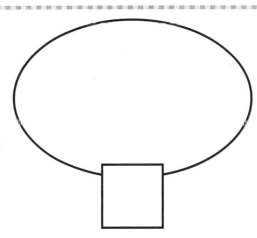

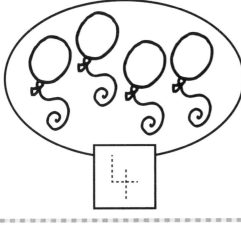

**4**

is the same as

**=**

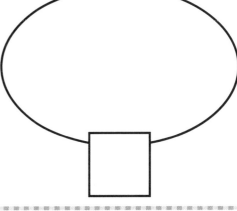

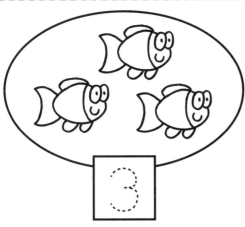

**3**

is the same as

**=**

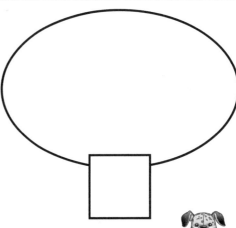

| Strand | Number |
|---|---|
| Strand Unit | Comparing |

**Objectives** Develop an understanding of the 'equals' symbol as meaning 'the same' or 'equivalent'.

35

# Add

$\boxed{1}$ and $\boxed{1} = \boxed{2}$

## Write the correct numerals. Add.

 and  =

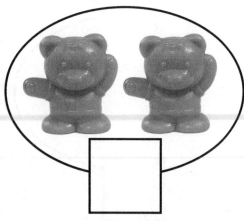 and  =

 and  =

 and 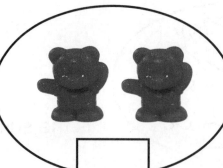 =

| | | |
|---|---|---|
| **Strand** | Number | |
| **Strand Unit** | Analysis of number | |

Objectives: Combining sets of objects using the 'equals' sign.

# Write the correct numerals. Add.

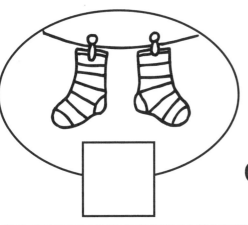

and

=

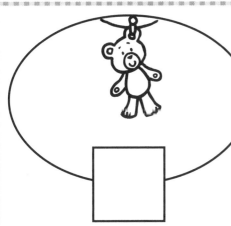

and

=

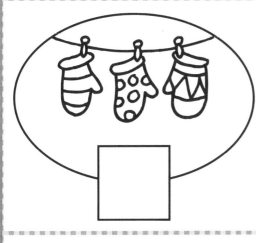

and

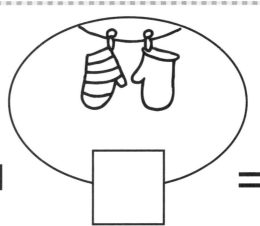

=

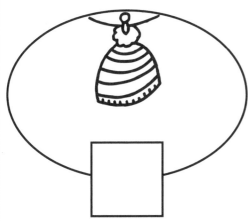

and

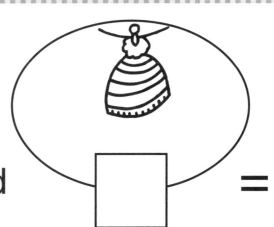

=

| Strand | Number | | Objectives | Combining sets of objects totals to 5 using the 'equals' sign. |
|--------|--------|--|------------|---|
| Strand Unit | Analysis of number | | | |

37

# Add

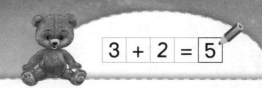 

## Add. Use your cubes.

$$2 \quad + \quad 1 \quad = \quad 3$$

| | | |
|---|---|---|
| 2 + 1 = 3 | 3 + 2 = ☐ |
| 2 + 2 = ☐ | 1 + 4 = ☐ |
| 1 + 2 = ☐ | 2 + 3 = ☐ |
| 3 + 1 = ☐ | 4 + 1 = ☐ |
| 1 + 1 = ☐ | 1 + 3 = ☐ |

## Make a colour pattern with the beads.

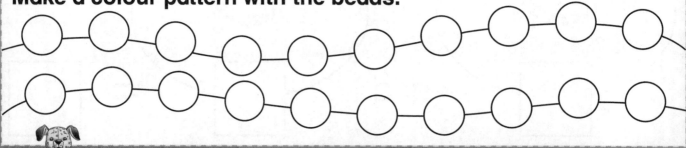

**38**

| | |
|---|---|
| **Strand** | Number |
| **Strand Unit** | Analysis of number |

Objectives: Combining sets of objects totals to 5 using the 'plus' and 'equals' signs.

5

## Draw different groups of spots for each number.

| 5 | ● ● ● ● ● | ● ● ● ● ● | |
| 4 | | | |
| 6 | | | |
| 3 | | | |

## Write the missing numerals.

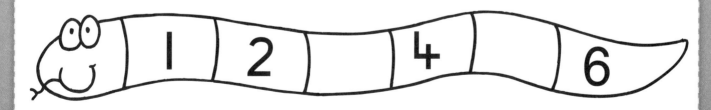

1  2  4  6

**Strand** Number
**Strand Unit** Counting

Objectives Present different patterns and arrays of the same number.

39

**Meet Zero. His shopping bag is empty!**

**Look in Zero's bag and count.**

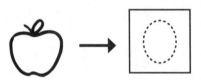 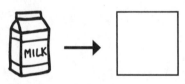 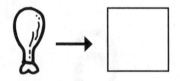

**Write the numeral.**

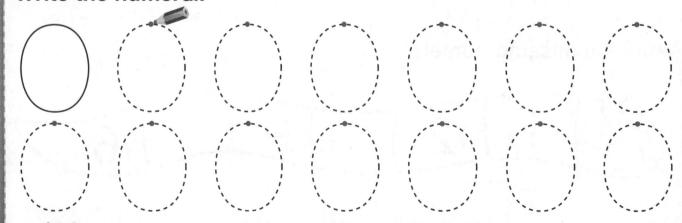

| Strand | Number | | Objectives | Identify the empty set and numeral zero. |
|---|---|---|---|---|
| Strand Unit | Numeration | | | |

## Write the numeral.

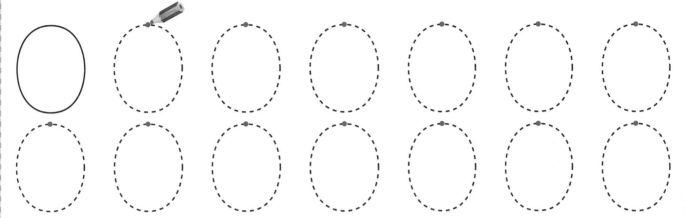

| | | | | | |
|---|---|---|---|---|---|
| 1 + 0 = | | | 0 + 1 = | |
| 2 + 0 = | | | 0 + 2 = | |
| 3 + 0 = | | | 0 + 3 = | |
| 4 + 0 = | | | 0 + 4 = | |
| 5 + 0 = | | | 0 + 5 = | |

## Write the missing numerals.

   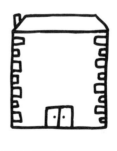 

0      2      4

0      1

| | |
|---|---|
| **Strand** | Number |
| **Strand Unit** | Numeration |

Objectives   Combining sets of objects including the 'empty set'.

41

# Add

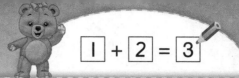

## How many ways can you put the **3** bears into the hula hoops?

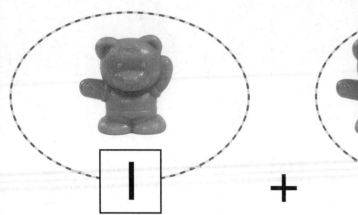

1 + 2 = ☐

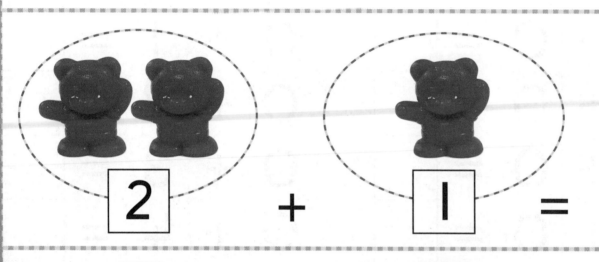

2 + 1 = ☐

0 + 3 = ☐

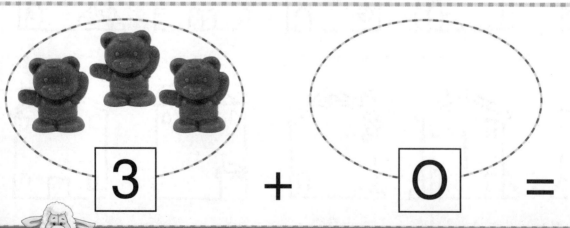

3 + 0 = ☐

| Strand | Number |
|---|---|
| Strand Unit | Analysis of number |

Objectives: Explore the components of number 3.

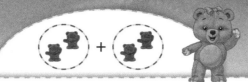

Here are **4** bears and **2** hula hoops. Use 5 cubes to help you.

How many ways can you put the **4** bears into the hula hoops?

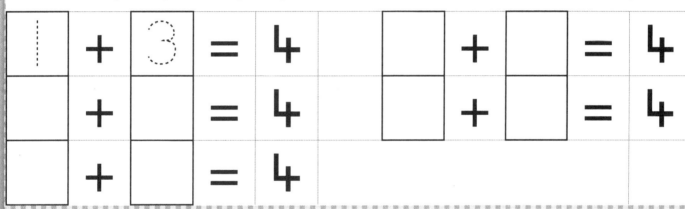

Draw **4** worms in the garden.

**Strand** Number
**Strand Unit** Analysis of number

Objectives  Explore the components of number 4.

# Add

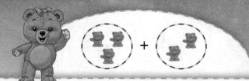

Here are **5** bears and **2** hula hoops.

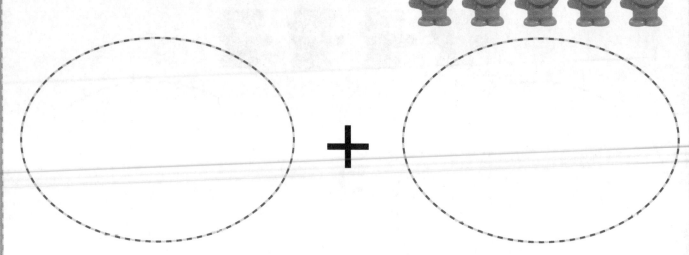

◯ **+** ◯

How many ways can you put the **5** bears into the hula hoops?

| | + | | = 5 |
|---|---|---|---|
| | + | | = 5 |
| | + | | = 5 |
| | + | | = 5 |
| | + | | = 5 |
| | + | | = 5 |

Draw **5** apples 🍎.

Write the numeral.

**Strand** Number
**Strand Unit** Analysis of number
Objectives Combining to explore the components of number 5.

How many ways can you put **5** spots on Butterfly's wings?
Use cubes or counters.

Write the story of 5.

| | + | | = 5 | | + | | = 5 |
| | + | | = 5 | | + | | = 5 |
| | + | | = 5 | | + | | = 5 |

Draw **5** buns .

# The Park

**Benny and Betsy are in the park. What can they see?**

**Colour the correct number of boxes.**

| | | | | | |
|---|---|---|---|---|---|
| 🦋 | | | | | |
| 🐌 | | | | | |
| 🦔 | | | | | |
| 🐟 | | | | | |
| 🐭 | | | | | |
| 🐰 | | | | | |

**Strand** Data
**Strand Unit** Recognising and interpreting data

Objectives
• Sort and classify groups of objects into sets.
• Represent data on a block graph.

## Count.

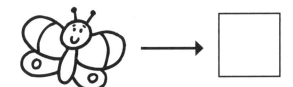

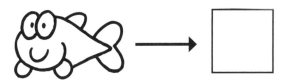

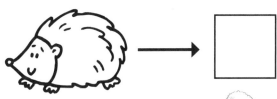

| Strand | Data |
| --- | --- |
| Strand Unit | Recognising and interpreting data |

Objectives
• Sort and classify groups of objects into sets.
• Represent data on a block graph.

47

# Add

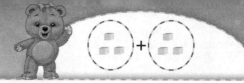

Here are **2** hula hoops. Here are **6** cubes.

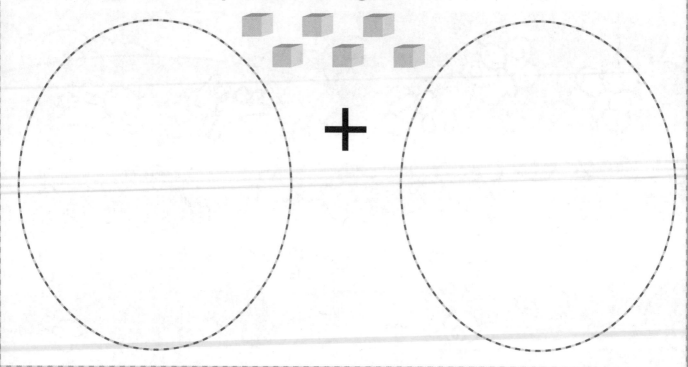

$+$

How many ways can you put the **6** cubes into the hula hoops?

| | | | | |
|---|---|---|---|---|
| | $+$ | | $=$ | 6 |
| | $+$ | | $=$ | 6 |
| | $+$ | | $=$ | 6 |
| | $+$ | | $=$ | 6 |
| | $+$ | | $=$ | 6 |
| | $+$ | | $=$ | 6 |
| | $+$ | | $=$ | 6 |

Draw **6** windows.

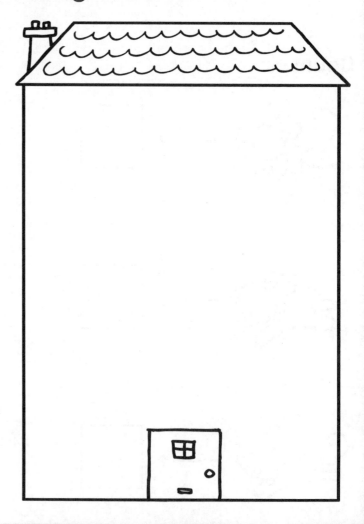

**Strand** Number
**Strand Unit** Analysis of number
Objectives Combining to explore the components of number 5.

How many ways can you put **6** spots on the sails? Use cubes.

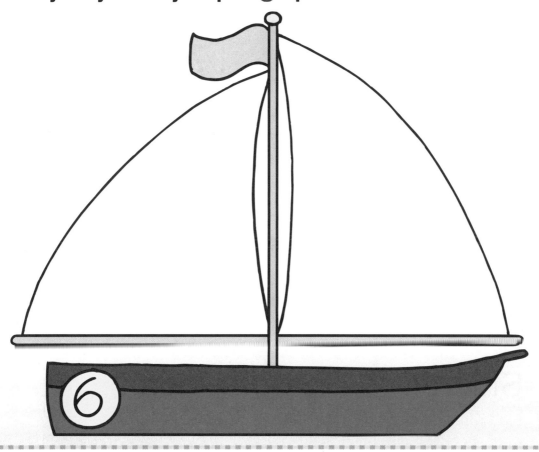

Write the story of **6**.

| | | | | | | | |
|---|---|---|---|---|---|---|---|
| ☐ | + | ☐ | = 6 | ☐ | + | ☐ | = 6 |
| ☐ | + | ☐ | = 6 | ☐ | + | ☐ | = 6 |
| ☐ | + | ☐ | = 6 | ☐ | + | ☐ | = 6 |
| ☐ | + | ☐ | = 6 | | | | |

Draw **6** ice-creams.

**Strand** Number
**Strand Unit** Analysis of number
Objectives Partitioning to explore the components of number 6.

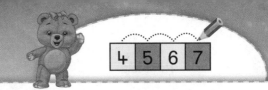

Start on **4**. Go on **2** more. 6

Start on **2**. Go on **4** more. ☐

Start on **3**. Go on **1** more. ☐

Start on **1**. Go on **2** more. ☐

Start on **4**. Go on **1** more. ☐

Start on **2**. Go on **3** more. ☐

Start on **5**. Go on **1** more. ☐

Start on **3**. Go on **3** more. ☐

| **Strand** | Number |
| **Strand Unit** | Analysis of number |

**Objectives** Combining numbers by counting 'on' on the number line, totals to 6.

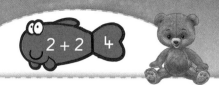

## Start on **2**. Go on **2** more. $\boxed{4}$

**Use the number line. Match the children and the fish. Colour.**

4   5   6

2 + 2   4

3 + 2

3 + 3

2 + 4

0 + 4

5 + 0

Colour:   4 → ●     5 → ●     6 → ●

| Strand | Number |
|---|---|
| Strand Unit | Analysis of number |

Objectives   Combining numbers totals to 6.

**51**

# Match

three

1

five

2

two

3

four

4

5

six

6

one

| Strand | Number |
| --- | --- |
| Strand Unit | Counting |

Objectives
- Count the number of items in a set totals to 6.
- Match to correct numeral.

# Meet the shape friends. Write their names.

## cube

C _ _ _ _ _

## cylinder

_ _ _ _ _ _ _ _ _

## sphere

_ _ _ _ _ _ _

## cuboid

_ _ _ _ _ _ _

**Strand** Shape and Space
**Strand Unit** 3D Shapes
**Objectives** Name and describe 3D shapes: cube, cuboid, sphere, and cylinder.

# Match

**Match each object to the correct shape.**

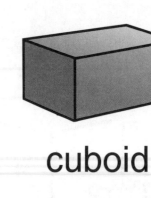

cuboid

sphere

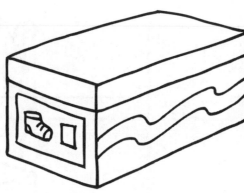
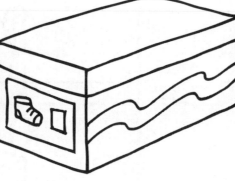

cube

cylinder

| Strand | Shape and Space |
|---|---|
| Strand Unit | 3D Shapes |

Objectives: Sort and name 3D shapes – cube, cuboid, sphere and cylinder.

**Can I roll along the floor? Tick ✓ Yes or No.**
**Use your shapes to check.**

cube

| yes | no ✓ |
|-----|------|

sphere

| yes | no |
|-----|-----|

cuboid

| yes | no |
|-----|-----|

cylinder

| yes | no |
|-----|-----|

| **Strand** | Shape and Space | Objectives | Describe 3D shapes according to attributes - flat, curved, can/can't roll. |
| **Strand Unit** | 3D Shapes | | |

55

# Add

$2 + 1 = 3$

## Use bears or cubes.

| | | | | |
|---|---|---|---|---|
| 1 | + | 2 | = | 3 |
| 4 | + | 2 | = | |
| 1 | + | 3 | = | |
| 5 | + | O | = | |
| 3 | + | 3 | = | |
| 1 | + | O | = | |

| | | | | |
|---|---|---|---|---|
| O | + | 2 | = | |
| 1 | + | 5 | = | |
| 2 | + | 4 | = | |
| 2 | + | 2 | = | |
| 3 | + | 1 | = | |
| 4 | + | 1 | = | |

## Add. Colour.

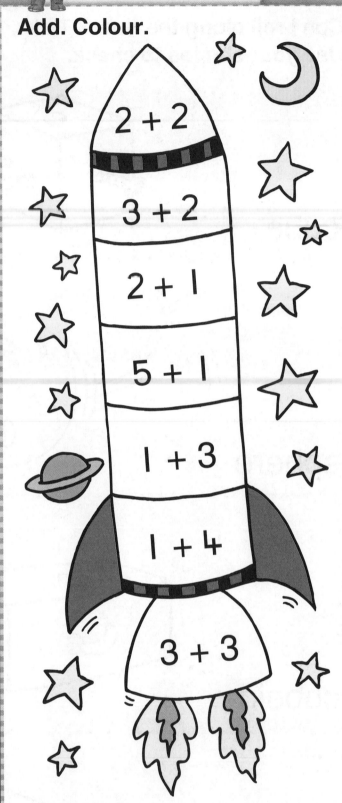

Colour key

4 → ●     5 → ●

3 → ●     6 → ●

| | |
|---|---|
| **Strand** | Number |
| **Strand Unit** | Analysis of number |

Objectives    Combining sets of objects totals to 6.

**Draw 7 apples on the tree. Draw 7 worms on the grass.**

## Write the numeral.

**Strand** Number
**Strand Unit** Counting

Objectives
• Counting up to 7.
• Writing the numeral 7.

**57**

# Draw

## Put **7** buttons  on each shirt.

## Colour the fish with **7** spots.

| Strand | Number | | Counting up to 7. |
|---|---|---|---|
| Strand Unit | Counting | | |

Objectives

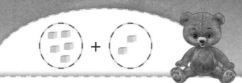

**Here are 2 hula hoops. Here are 7 cubes.**

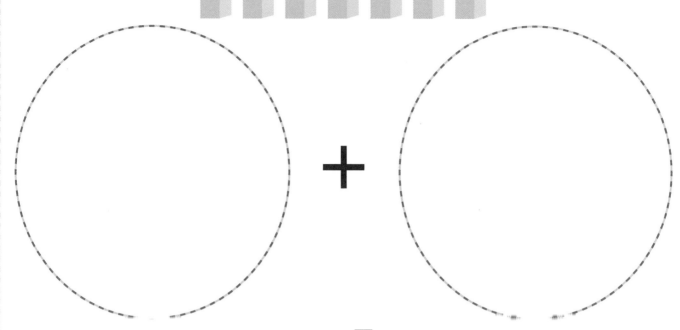

+

**How many ways can you put the 7 cubes into the hula hoops?**

| | + | | = 7 | | + | | = 7 |
|---|---|---|---|---|---|---|---|
| | + | | = 7 | | + | | = 7 |
| | + | | = 7 | | + | | = 7 |
| | + | | = 7 | | + | | = 7 |

**Draw 7 lollipops.**

How many ways can you put **7** spots on Ladybird's wings?
Use counters.

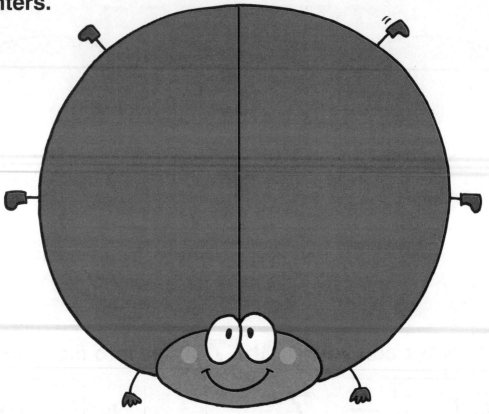

Write the story of **7**.

| | + | | = 7 | | + | | = 7 |
|---|---|---|---|---|---|---|---|
| | + | | = 7 | | + | | = 7 |
| | + | | = 7 | | + | | = 7 |
| | + | | = 7 | | + | | = 7 |

Draw **7** triangles △. Colour each one differently.

| Strand | Number | | Objectives | Partitioning to explore the components of 7. |
|---|---|---|---|---|
| Strand Unit | Analysis of number | | | |

**Colour the pairs of socks that make 7. Use your cubes to help.**

3 + 4     1 + 4     2 + 4

6 + 1     0 + 7     3 + 2

Benny wants **7** sweets in each bag. How many sweets must he add to each bag? Write sums under the bags.

3 + 4 = 7     5 + ☐ = 7

6 + ☐ = 7     2 + ☐ = 7

**Strand** Number
**Strand Unit** Analysis of number
Objectives Partitioning to explore the components of 7.
61

# Add

## Add on the number strip.

Start on **2**. Go on **2** more. ☐ 4

## Match the kites and the children.

| Strand | Number | | Combining numbers totals to 7. |
| Strand Unit | Analysis of number | | |

**2** boats.

**Draw** more than **2** boats.

**4** lollipops.

**Draw** more than **4** lollipops.

**6** balls.

**Draw** more than **6** balls.

**Strand** Number
**Strand Unit** Comparing and ordering
Objectives Compare non-equivalent sets 0 – 10.
**63**

# Add

**Kitty has 4 lollipops.**
**Emma has 3 lollipops.**

They have [ ] lollipops altogether.

**Alex has 3 balloons.**
**Max has 3 balloons.**

They have [ ] balloons altogether.

**The clown has 4 hats.**
**The dog has 1 hat.**

They have [ ] hats altogether.

**Zack has 2 pencils.**
**Anna has 2 pencils.**

They have [ ] pencils altogether.

**Ben has 5 buns.**
**Kim has 0 buns.**

They have [ ] buns altogether.

| Strand | Number |
| --- | --- |
| Strand Unit | Numeration |

Objectives    Solve simple story problems totals to 7.

first      second      third      last

The 🐱 cat is _____.

The 🐸 frog is _____.

The 🐻 bear is _____.

The 🐰 rabbit is _____.

| **first** | **last** |
|:---:|:---:|

The 🐻 bear is _____.

The 🐱 cat is _____.

**Strand** Number
**Strand Unit** Comparing and ordering

Objectives — Use ordinal number to describe position in a line – first, second, third, last.

65

# Colour

**Colour the first person green. Colour the last person blue.**

| first | second | third | last |
|:-----:|:------:|:-----:|:----:|

**Colour.**

SPORTS DAY

| Strand | Number |
|---|---|
| Strand Unit | Comparing |

Objectives: Use the language of ordinal number to describe position in a line – first, second, third, last.

# Write

## Write and colour.

first →     second →     third →

| | | |
|---|---|---|
| | | |

## Draw.

Put a  on the first step.

Put a  on the second step.

Put an  on the third step.

Put a  on the last step.

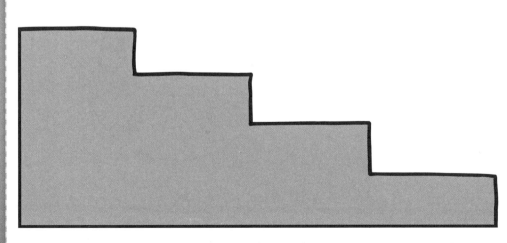

**Strand** Number
**Strand Unit** Comparing and ordering
Objectives — Use the language of ordinal number to describe position.

67

# Add

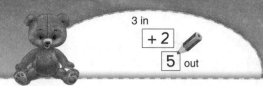

## The adding machine.

3 in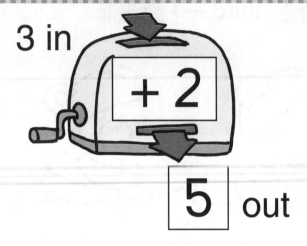

5 out

2 in

out

I in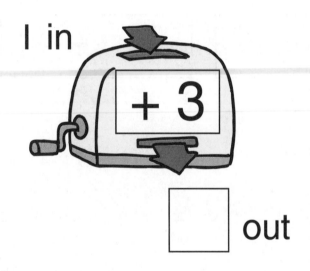

out

O in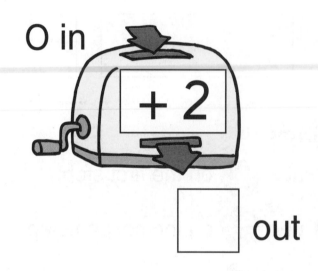

out

## Add the numbers on the wheels.

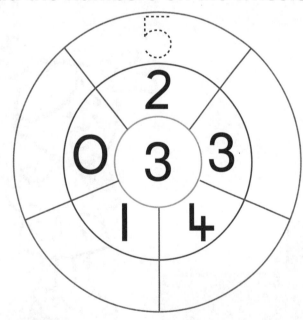

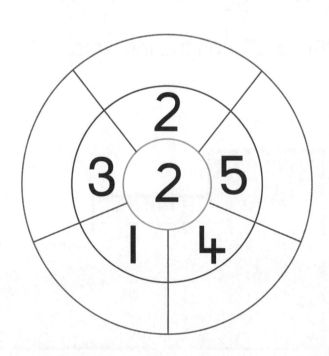

| Strand | Number | Objectives | Combine sets of objects, totals to seven. |
| --- | --- | --- | --- |
| Strand Unit | Analysis of number | | |

**3** kites.

Draw less than **3** kites.

**5** apples.

Draw less than **5** apples.

**7** fish.

Draw less than **7** fish.

| | |
|---|---|
| **Strand** | Number |
| **Strand Unit** | Comparing and ordering |

Objectives   Compare non-equivalent sets 0 – 10.

## Kim has 6 socks. Alex has 3 socks.

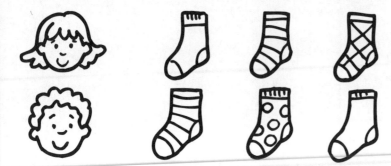

Alex has ☐ socks **less than** Kim.

## Ben has 7 lollipops. Emma has 5 lollipops.

Emma has ☐ lollipops **less than** Ben.

## Zack has 9 apples. Max has 3 apples.

Max has ☐ apples **less than** Zack.

| Strand | Number |
| --- | --- |
| Strand Unit | Numeration |

Objectives    Solve simple story problems.

**Draw 8 legs ⟨⟩ on Olly Octopus. Draw 8 fish beside him.**

## Write the numeral.

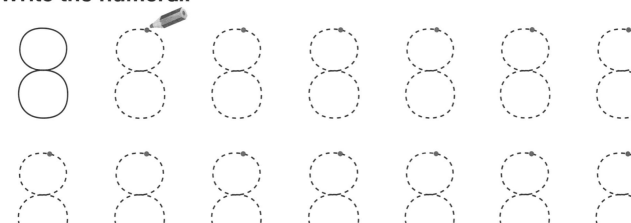

| Strand | Number |
| --- | --- |
| Strand Unit | Counting |

Objectives
• Counting up to 8.
• Writing the numeral 8.

71

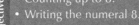

# Draw

**Draw 8 spots 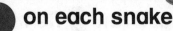 on each snake.**

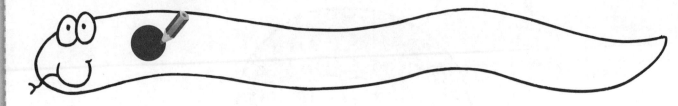

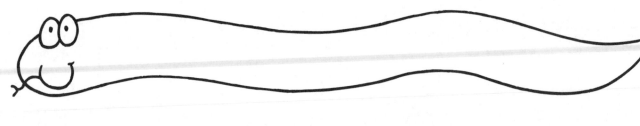

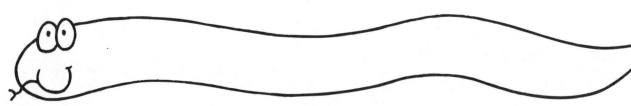

**Colour the monsters with 8 teeth.**

| Strand | Number | | Counting up to 8. |
|---|---|---|---|
| Strand Unit | Counting | Objectives | |

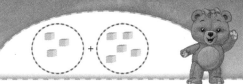

**Here are 2 hula hoops. Here are 8 cubes.**

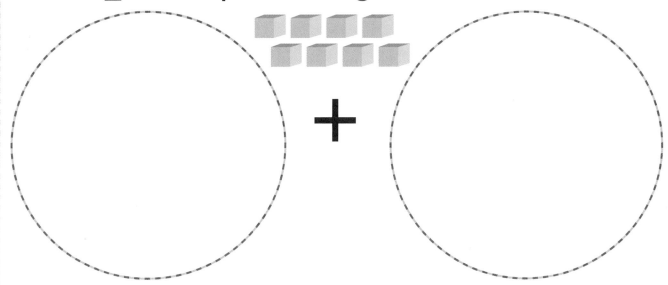

**+**

**How many ways can you put the 8 cubes into the hula hoops?**

| | | | | | | | |
|---|---|---|---|---|---|---|---|
| ☐ | + | ☐ | = | 8 | ☐ | + | ☐ | = 8 |
| ☐ | + | ☐ | = | 8 | ☐ | + | ☐ | = 8 |
| ☐ | + | ☐ | = | 8 | ☐ | + | ☐ | = 8 |
| ☐ | + | ☐ | = | 8 | ☐ | + | ☐ | = 8 |
| ☐ | + | ☐ | = | 8 | | | | |

**Draw 8 trees 🌳.**

**Strand** Number
**Strand Unit** Analysis of number
Objectives Combining to explore the components of number 8.

73

How many ways can you put **8** spots on Benny's tie? Use cubes.

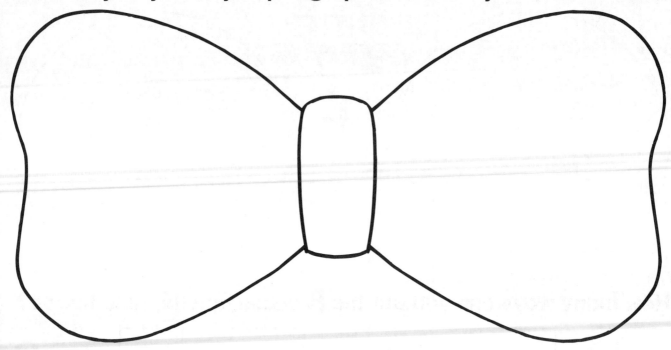

**Write the story of 8.**

| | + | | = 8 | | + | | = 8 |
|---|---|---|---|---|---|---|---|
| | + | | = 8 | | + | | = 8 |
| | + | | = 8 | | + | | = 8 |
| | + | | = 8 | | + | | = 8 |
| | + | | = 8 | | | | |

**Draw 8 squares □. Colour each one differently.**

| Strand | Number |
|---|---|
| Strand Unit | Analysis of number |

Objectives: Partitioning to explore the components of number 8.

$3 + 5 = 8$

# How many sweets must you add to each plate to make **8**?
# Write a sum under each plate.

 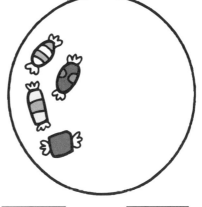

$3$ + $5$ = $8$     $4$ + $\square$ = $8$

$5$ + $\square$ = $8$     $2$ + $\square$ = $8$

 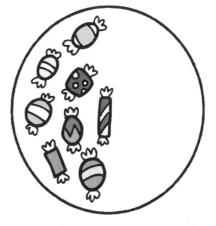

$7$ + $\square$ = $8$     $8$ + $\square$ = $8$

**Strand** Number
**Strand Unit** Analysis of number
Objectives   Combining to explore the components of 8.

**75**

# The Toybox

**Draw these toys in the toy box.**

   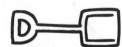

| **Strand** | Data | **Objectives** | Represent and interpret data in rows. |
| **Strand Unit** | Recognising and interpreting data | | |

**How many? Colour the correct amount of boxes.**

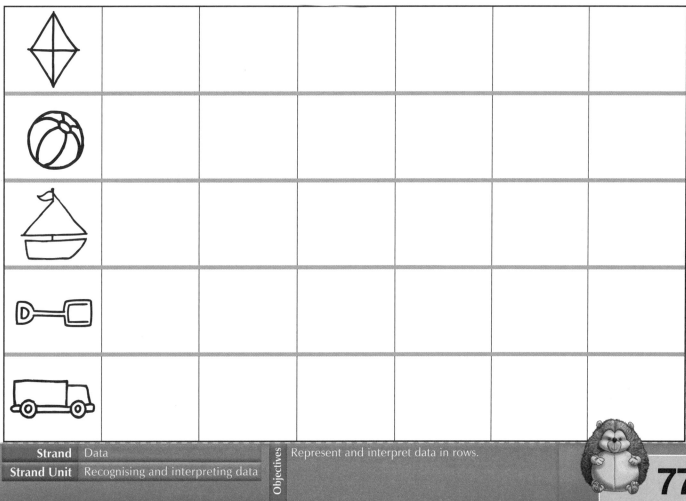

**Emma has 4 sweets. Kim has 3 sweets.**

How many have they altogether?

**Denis has 5 lollipops. Alex gives him 2 more.**

How many has Denis now?

**Max has 6 eggs. Mum has 4 eggs.**

How many have they altogether?

**Meg has 3 buns. Dad gives her 2 more.**

How many has she now?

| Strand | Number |
| --- | --- |
| Strand Unit | Numeration |

Objectives Solve simple 'story problems', totals to 8.

**Draw 9 worms in this garden.**

**Write the numeral.**

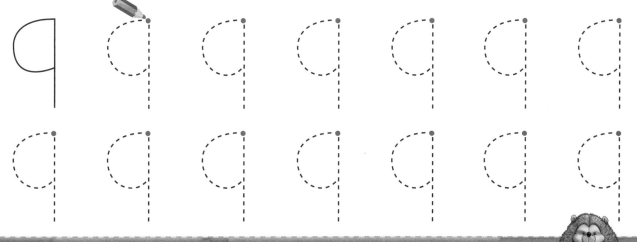

| Strand | Number |
| --- | --- |
| Strand Unit | Counting |

Objectives
- Counting to 9.
- Writing the numeral 9.

# Draw

Draw **9** beads on each string. Make a pattern.

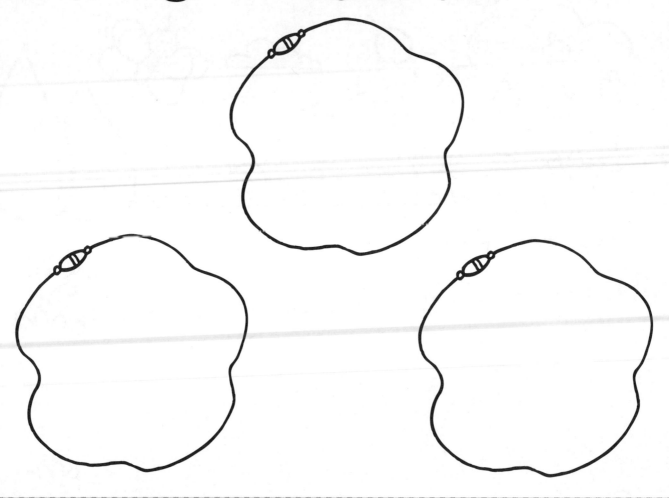

Colour the snakes with **9** spots.

| Strand | Number | | Counting to 9. |
|---|---|---|---|
| **Strand Unit** | Counting | | |

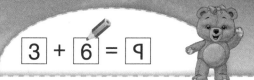

$3 + 6 = 9$

Add

## Here are **2** hula hoops. Here are **9** cubes.

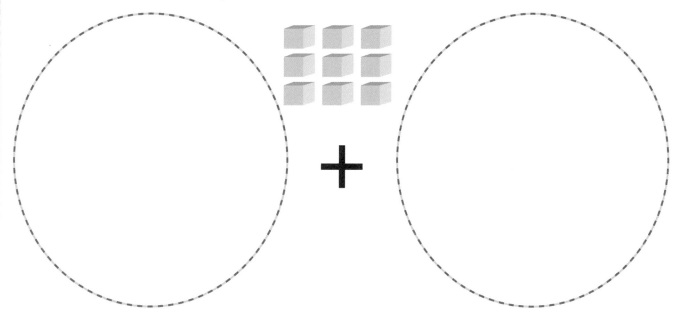

+

How many ways can you put the **9** cubes into the hula hoops?

|   | + |   | = | 9 |   |   | + |   | = | 9 |
|---|---|---|---|---|---|---|---|---|---|---|
|   | + |   | = | 9 |   |   | + |   | = | 9 |
|   | + |   | = | 9 |   |   | + |   | = | 9 |
|   | + |   | = | 9 |   |   | + |   | = | 9 |
|   | + |   | = | 9 |   |   | + |   | = | 9 |

Draw **9** happy faces ☺.

**Strand** Number

**Strand Unit** Analysis of number

Objectives    Combining to explore the components of number 9.

81

**Find different ways to put 9 spots on Benny's umbrella. Use counters.**

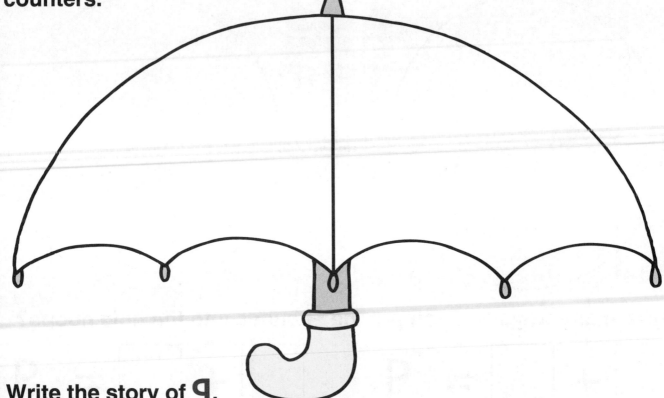

**Write the story of 9.**

| | + | | = | 9 | | + | | = | 9 |
| | + | | = | 9 | | + | | = | 9 |
| | + | | = | 9 | | + | | = | 9 |
| | + | | = | 9 | | + | | = | 9 |
| | + | | = | 9 | | + | | = | 9 |

**Write the numeral.**

| Strand | Number |
|---|---|
| Strand Unit | Analysis of number |

Objectives: Partitioning to explore components of number 9.

## Colour the pairs that make 9. Use your cubes.

| 3 + | 6 |
| 4 + | 2 |
| 7 + | 2 |

| 5 + | 4 |
| 1 + | 7 |
| 6 + | 3 |

## Tick ✓ the correct sums. ✗ the incorrect sums.

3 + 6 = 9 ✓          1 + 8 = 9

4 + 4 = 9          5 + 4 = 9

7 + 2 = 9          2 + 4 = 9

| Strand | Number |
| Strand Unit | Analysis of number |

Objectives: Combining to explore the components of number 9.

83

# Seasons

 spring  summer  autumn winter

**Write the correct word.**

**Strand** Measures
**Strand Unit** Time

Objectives Develop understanding of the concept of time –
seasons, significant events, festivals, holidays.

Thursday

Wednesday

Friday

Tuesday

Saturday

Monday

Sunday

**Write.**

Today is _____.

Yesterday was _____.

Tomorrow will be _____.

I like _____ best.

We have no school on _____ and _____ .

Strand   Measures
Strand Unit   Time

Objectives   • Develop an understanding of the concept of time.
• Sequence weekly events.

85

# Clocks

**Draw the hour hand on each clock.**

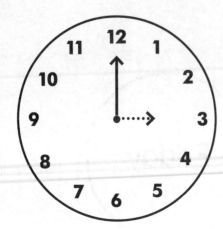

3 o'clock

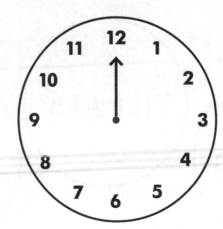

9 o'clock

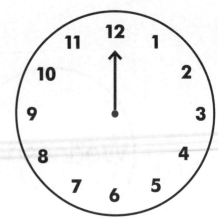

5 o'clock

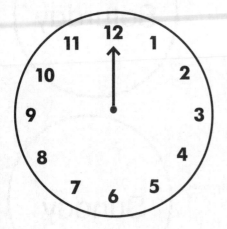

7 o'clock

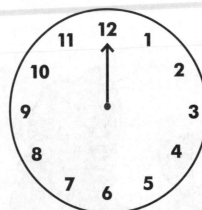

2 o'clock

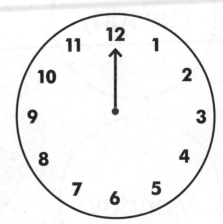

6 o'clock

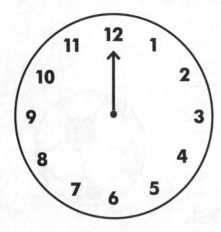

12 o'clock

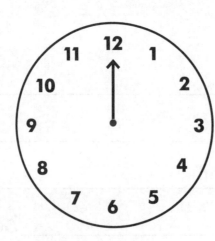

8 o'clock

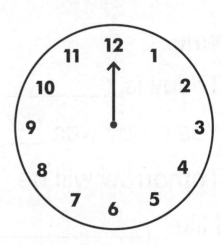

10 o'clock

| Strand | Measures |
| --- | --- |
| Strand Unit | Time |

Objectives  Read the time in one hour intervals.

**Draw the hour hand in black. Draw the minute hand in blue.**

morning

_ _ _ _ _ _ _ _

9 o'clock

afternoon

_ _ _ _ _ _ _ _ _ _

3 o'clock

evening

_ _ _ _ _ _ _ _ _

5 o'clock

night

_ _ _ _ _

8 o'clock

| Strand | Measures |
|---|---|
| Strand Unit | Time |

Objectives: Discuss significant times in a day, record orally and pictorially the time sequence of four events in the day.

87

# Draw

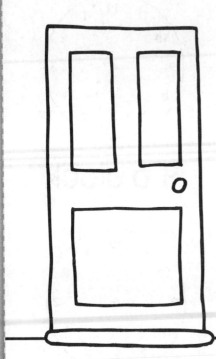

1. Draw a ▨ **on** the 〰️.

2. Draw a ⬠ **under** the ⊞.

3. Draw a 🪑 **beside** the 🚪.

4. Draw 〰️ **on** the ⊞.

5. Draw a 🧺 **beside** the 🪑.

| Strand | Shape and Space |
|---|---|
| Strand Unit | Spatial Awareness |

Objectives: Explore, discuss, develop and use the language of spatial relations.

**Match the pictures and words.**

**on**

**between**

**under**

**Strand** Shape and Space
**Strand Unit** Spatial Awareness

Objectives

Explore, discuss, develop and use the language of spatial relations.

# Colour

**Colour the bears in front of the wall red.**
**Colour the bears behind the wall blue.**

**Draw 1 snail**  **between the flowers.**

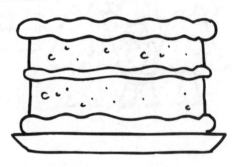

**Draw 4 candles** on the cake.

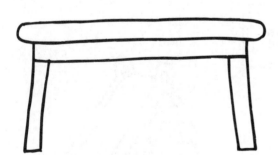

**Draw 1 cat**  **under the table.**

**Draw 3 eggs** in the nest.

**Strand** Shape and Space
**Strand Unit** Spatial Awareness

Objectives Explore, discuss, develop and use the language of spatial relations.

**Draw 10 balls for Betsy Bear.**

**Write the numeral.**

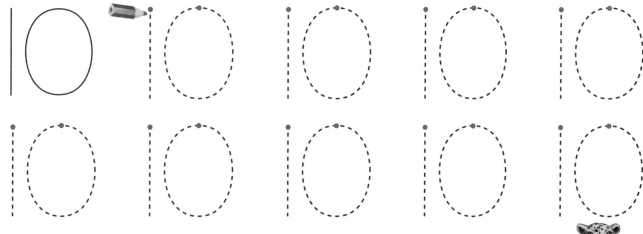

# Draw

**Draw 10 steps on each ladder.**

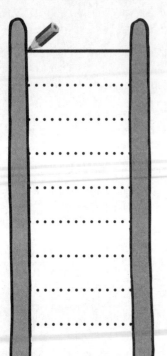

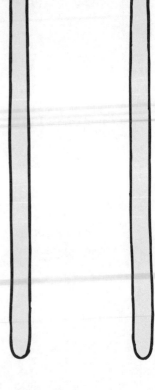

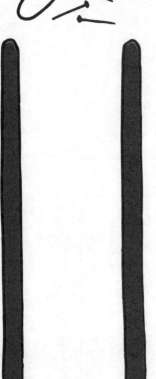

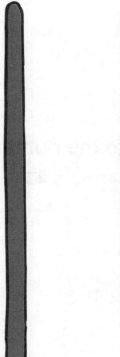

| Strand | Number | Objectives | Counting to 10. |
|---|---|---|---|
| Strand Unit | Counting | | |

$\boxed{4} + \boxed{6} = 10$

## Here are **2** hula hoops and **10** cubes.

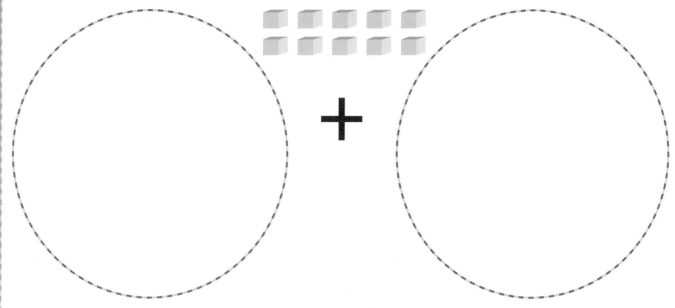

$+$

How many ways can you put the **10** cubes into the hula hoops?

| | + | | = 10 | | + | | = 10 |
|---|---|---|---|---|---|---|---|
| | + | | = 10 | | + | | = 10 |
| | + | | = 10 | | + | | = 10 |
| | + | | = 10 | | + | | = 10 |
| | + | | = 10 | | + | | = 10 |
| | + | | = 10 | | | | |

Draw **10** lollipops.

**Strand**  Number
**Strand Unit**  Analysis of number
Objectives  Exploring the components of 10.

**93**

# Number 10

$$\boxed{3} + \boxed{7} = 10$$

**How many ways can you put 10 pips on this apple? Use cubes.**

**Write the story of 10.**

| | + | | = | 10 | | + | | = | 10 |
|---|---|---|---|---|---|---|---|---|---|
| | + | | = | 10 | | + | | = | 10 |
| | + | | = | 10 | | + | | = | 10 |
| | + | | = | 10 | | + | | = | 10 |
| | + | | = | 10 | | + | | = | 10 |
| | + | | = | 10 | | | | | |

**Write the missing numerals.**

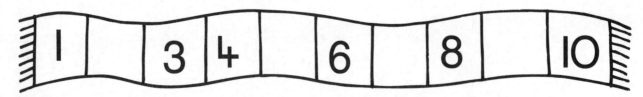

| 1 | | 3 | 4 | | 6 | | 8 | | 10 |
|---|---|---|---|---|---|---|---|---|---|

**94**

| **Strand** | Number |
|---|---|
| **Strand Unit** | Analysis of number |

Objectives: Partitioning to explore the components of number 10.

**Benny wants 10 beads on each string. Can you help him?**

$$\boxed{5} + \boxed{5} = \boxed{10}$$

---

**Draw the missing beads. Write a sum for each string.**

$$\boxed{7} + \boxed{\phantom{0}} = 10 \qquad \boxed{4} + \boxed{\phantom{0}} = 10$$

$$\boxed{3} + \boxed{\phantom{0}} = 10 \qquad \boxed{8} + \boxed{\phantom{0}} = 10$$

$$\boxed{2} + \boxed{\phantom{0}} = 10 \qquad \boxed{1} + \boxed{\phantom{0}} = 10$$

**Strand** Number
**Strand Unit** Analysis of number
Objectives   Combining to explore the components of 10.

95

# Add

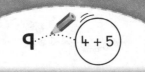

## Match the children and the footballs. Add on the number line.

$$0 \quad 1 \quad 2 \quad 3 \quad 4 \quad 5 \quad 6 \quad 7 \quad 8 \quad 9 \quad 10$$

### Start on **7**. Go on **2** more.

9

10   9   7

7 + 2

2 + 5

5 + 5

8 + 2

6 + 3

4 + 5

1 + 9

1 + 6

6 + 4

3 + 4

| Strand | Number |
| Strand Unit | Analysis of number |

Objectives  Combining number totals to 10.

$4 + 1 = 5$

## Add the numbers on the wheels. Use your cubes.

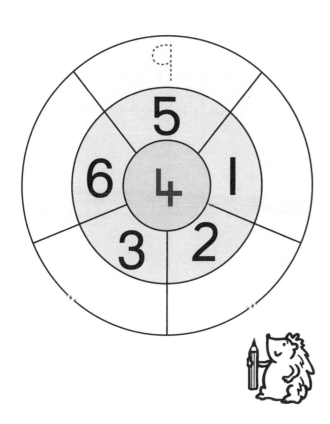

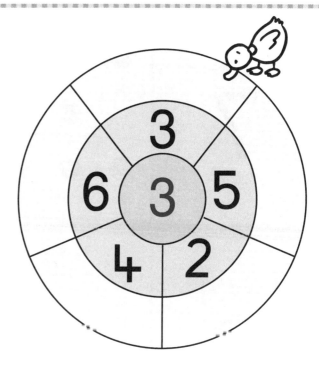

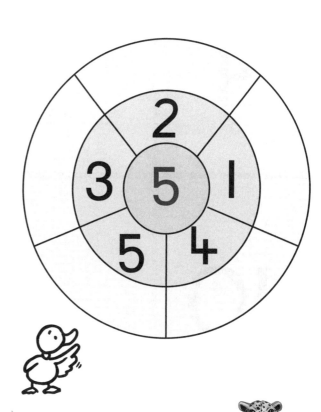

| Strand | Number |
|---|---|
| Strand Unit | Analysis of number |

Objectives — Combining sets of objects, totals to 10.

# Draw

**7** ∴∵

Draw groups of spots for each numeral.

| | | | |
|---|---|---|---|
| **7** | ● ● ●<br>●<br>● ● | | |
| **8** | | | |
| **9** | | | |
| **10** | | | |

| Strand | Number |
|---|---|
| Strand Unit | Counting |

Objectives: Present different patterns and arrays of the same number.

Start on **3**. Go on **2** more.  | 5 |  | 3 + 2 = 5 |

## Write each sum.

Start on **6**. Go on **1** more.  | 7 |  | 6 + 1 = 7 |

Start on **3**. Go on **2** more.

Start on **3**. Go on **3** more.

Start on **4**. Go on **1** more.

Start on **5**. Go on **3** more.

Start on **2**. Go on **2** more.

Start on **6**. Go on **4** more.

Start on **3**. Go on **6** more.

**Strand** Number
**Strand Unit** Analysis of number
Objectives   Adding on the number line by counting on.

99

# Number Line

0 1 2 3 4 5 6 7 8 9 10

**Start on 3. Go on 3 more.**

| 6 | 3 + 3 = 6 |

**Write the sum.**

0 1 2 3 4 5 6 7 8 9 10

Start on **4**. Go on **1** more.

Start on **7**. Go on **2** more.

Start on **8**. Go on **2** more.

Start on **3**. Go on **4** more.

Start on **2**. Go on **7** more.

Start on **4**. Go on **4** more.

Start on **7**. Go on **3** more.

Start on **1**. Go on **3** more.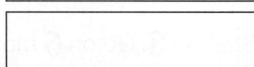

Strand   Number
Strand Unit   Analysis of number

Objectives   Adding on the number line by counting on.

| 0 | 1 | 2 | 3 | 4 | 5 | 6 | 7 | 8 | 9 | 10 |

**Start**         **Start**

| Start | | | Start | | |
|---|---|---|---|---|---|
| 1 | go on 1 → | 2 | 6 | go on 2 → | |
| 2 | → | | 4 | → | |
| 4 | → | | 3 | → | |
| 3 | → | | 5 | → | |
| 0 | → | | 2 | → | |
| 7 | → | | 0 | → | |

## Write the missing numerals.

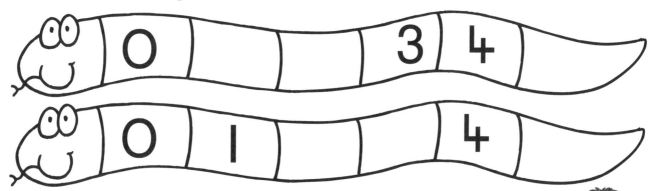

| | 0 | | | 3 | 4 | |
| | 0 | 1 | | | 4 | |

**Strand** Number
**Strand Unit** Analysis of number

Objectives
• Counting on the number line.
• Filling in the missing numbers.

101

# Add

**Match each dog to the correct bone. Use the number line.**

0  1  2  3  4  5  6  7  8  9  10

Start on **4**. Go on **1** more.　5

4 + 1　　5　　4 + 4

5 + 3　　8　　5 + 1

3 + 3　　10　　3 + 2

2 + 8　　6　　6 + 4

| Strand | Number |
| --- | --- |
| **Strand Unit** | Analysis of number |

Objectives　Combining numbers totals to 10.

## Draw the correct amount of spots on each rectangle.

one

two

three

four

five

six

seven

eight

nine

ten

## Draw the correct amount of spots on each ladybird.

5

— — — —

10

— — — —

6

— — — —

8

— — — —

# Colour

Baby Bear

Mammy Bear

Daddy Bear

**blue**

**yellow**

**red**

---

**Colour Baby Bear blue, Mammy Bear yellow and Daddy Bear red.**

| Strand | Measures | Objectives | Compare and order objects according to height. |
| Strand Unit | Length | | |

**Draw a bigger circle.**

**Draw a shorter line.**

**Draw a smaller fish.**

**Draw a longer snake.**

**Draw a taller tree.**

**Draw a smaller box.**

| Strand | Measures |
|---|---|
| Strand Unit | Length |

Objectives: Compare and order objects according to height and length.

# Measure

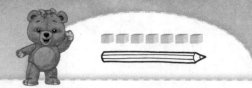

**Measure with cubes. Write each amount.**

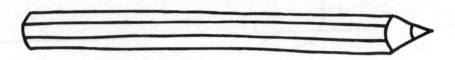

my estimate [ ]          cubes [ ]

my estimate [ ]          cubes [ ]

my estimate [ ]          cubes [ ]

my estimate [ ]          cubes [ ]

**Strand** Measures
**Strand Unit** Length

Objectives    Estimate and measure length in non-standard units.

## Measure the distance from Betsy to her toys. Use cubes. Record.

Start here

---

 →

my estimate     cubes

---

 →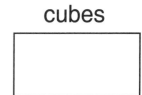

my estimate     cubes

---

 →

my estimate     cubes

---

 →

my estimate     cubes

**Strand** Measures
**Strand Unit** Length
Objectives Estimate and measure length in non-standard units.

107

# Match

**Match the coins to the correct amount of cent.**

                                    2c

                                    5c

 ..................................  1c

                                    20c

                                    10c

**Write the correct amount under each coin.**

_____C    _____C    _____C    _____C    _____C

108

Strand   Measures
Strand Unit   Money
Objectives   Recognise coins up to 20c.

## Colour

### Colour the correct amount in each row.

### Draw the correct amount in each piggy bank.

2c      3c      4c

**Strand** Measures
**Strand Unit** Money
Objectives: Use coins in shopping activity, tender appropriate coins.

## How much in each piggy bank?

**A**

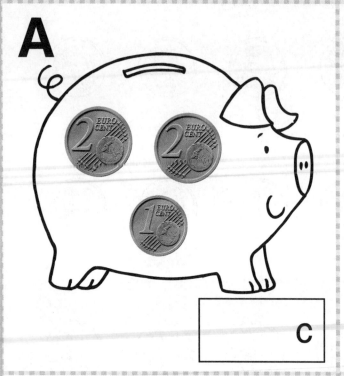

C

**B**

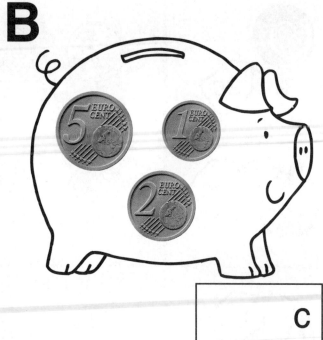

C

**C**

C

**D**

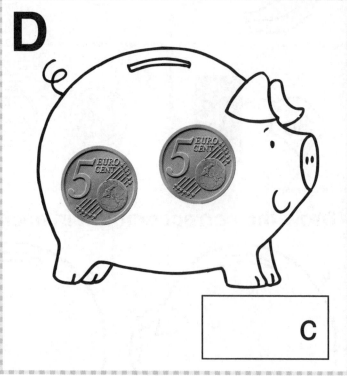

C

Which piggy bank has the **most** money?

Which piggy bank has the **least** money?

| Strand | Measures | Objectives | Add coins up to totals 10c. |
|--------|----------|------------|------------------------------|
| Strand Unit | Money | | |

$$\begin{array}{r} 3c \\ + 5c \\ \hline 8c \end{array}$$

SWEET SHOP

## Ben buys

| | | |
|---|---|---|
| 🍌 | 3 | c |
| 🍦 | + 5 | c |
| He spends | ☐ | c |

## Evan buys

| | | |
|---|---|---|
| 🍬 | 2 | c |
| 🧁 | + 3 | c |
| He spends | ☐ | c |

## Anna buys

| | | |
|---|---|---|
| 🍫 | 4 | c |
| 🥔 | + 6 | c |
| She spends | ☐ | c |

## Liam buys

| | | |
|---|---|---|
| 🧁 | 3 | c |
| 🍌 | + 3 | c |
| He spends | ☐ | c |

**Who spent the most money?** _____

**Who spent the least money?** _____

**Strand** Measures
**Strand Unit** Money

Objectives

Complete practical shopping tasks and problems using money to total of 10.

111

# Match

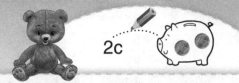

**Match each child to the correct piggy bank.**

Evan has 10c.

Anna has 7c.

Emma has 2c.

Max has 6c.

_____ has the **most** money.

_____ has the **least** money.

| Strand | Measures | | Recognise and use coins up to 10c. |
|---|---|---|---|
| Strand Unit | Money | | |

# How much money did Betsy Bear spend?

SWEET SHOP

C

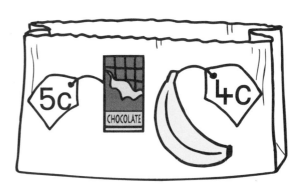

C

C

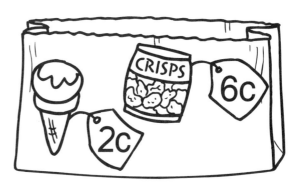

C

# Add

## The shop

 3c
 4c
 2c

 5c
 5c
 3c
 6c

**Betsy has 9c. What can she buy? Tick ✓ yes or no.**

3c + 4c + 2c

yes
no

5c + 2c + 2c

yes
no

3c + 2c + 5c

yes
no

2c + 6c + 2c

yes
no

5c + 2c + 3c

yes
no

| Strand | Measures |
| Strand Unit | Money |

Objectives Complete practical shopping tasks using money to totals 10c.

## Count on the number line.

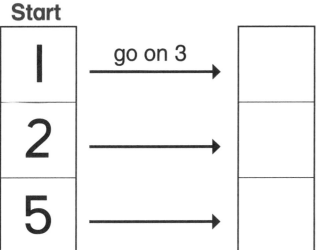

| 0 | 1 | 2 | 3 | 4 | 5 | 6 | 7 | 8 | 9 | 10 |

**Start**

| 1 | go on 3 → | |
| 2 | → | |
| 5 | → | |
| 0 | → | |
| 7 | → | |
| 4 | → | |
| 3 | → | |

**Start**

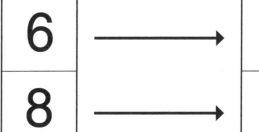

| 5 | go on 1 → | |
| 3 | → | |
| 2 | → | |
| 4 | → | |
| 6 | → | |
| 8 | → | |
| 7 | → | |

## Write the missing numerals.

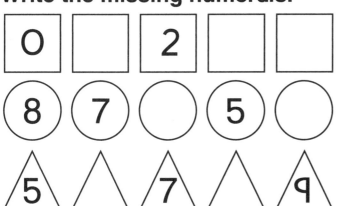

| 0 | | 2 | | |

8  7  ◯  5  ◯

5  △  7  △  9

**Strand** Number
**Strand Unit** Analysis of number
**Objectives** Counting on the number line.

115

# The Fair

## How many?

🌸 → ☐   🦆 → ☐   ▽ → ☐

🍭 → ☐   CRISPS → ☐   🐦 → ☐

---

**Tick** ✓

Can the cube  roll down the hill?

| yes |
| --- |
| no |

Can the sphere  roll down the hill?

| yes |
| --- |
| no |

Strand   Multiple
Strand Unit   Counting

Objectives   Counting sets of objects totals to eight.

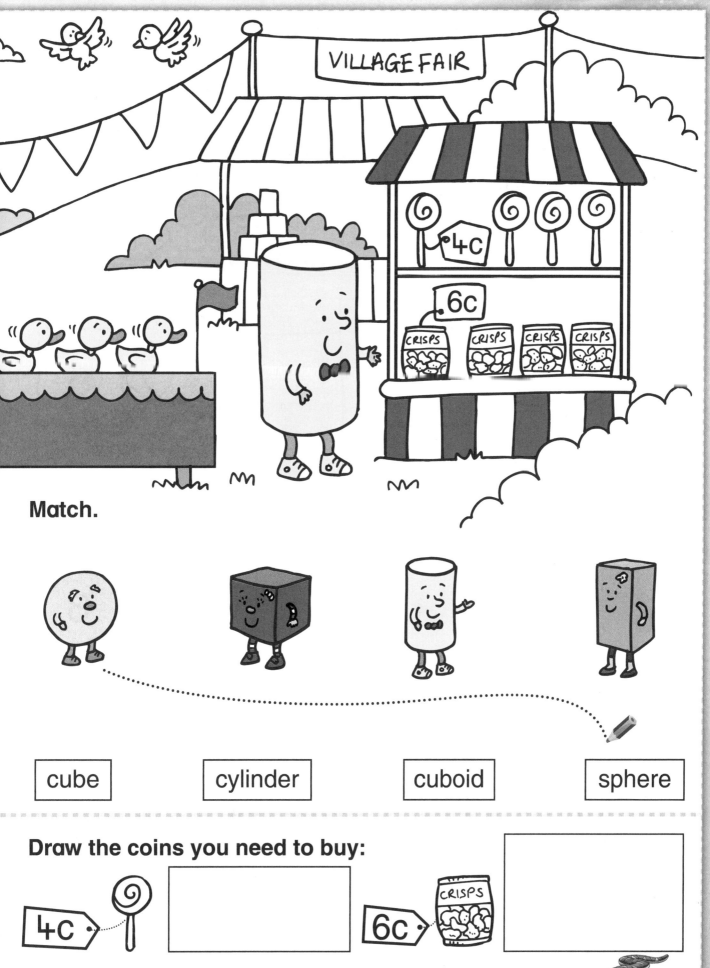

VILLAGE FAIR

4C

6c

CRISPS CRISPS CRISPS CRISPS

**Match.**

| cube | cylinder | cuboid | sphere |

---

**Draw the coins you need to buy:**

4C

6C

CRISPS

**Strand** Multiple
**Strand Unit** 3D Shapes
Objectives Sort and name 3D shapes, cube, cuboid, sphere and cylinder.

117

# Colour

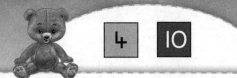

**Colour the higher numeral red. Colour the lower numeral blue.**

4 | 10

4 | 1

9 | 6

1 | 5

6 | 8

2 | 3

5 | 7

6 | 3

| Strand | Number |
| --- | --- |
| Strand Unit | Comparing and ordering |

Objectives — Compare and order numbers up to 10.

## Start with the higher number. Count on the number line.

| 0 | 1 | 2 | 3 | 4 | 5 | 6 | 7 | 8 | 9 | 10 |

$4 + 3 = 7$

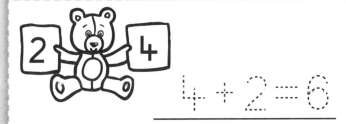

$4 + 2 = 6$

_____

_____

_____

_____

_____

_____

_____

_____

**Strand** Number
**Strand Unit** Analysis of number
Objectives
Adding on the number line, beginning with the higher number.

# Add

## Start with the higher number. Count on the number line.

| 0 | 1 | 2 | 3 | 4 | 5 | 6 | 7 | 8 | 9 | 10 |

  6  3

  1  4

$6 + 3 = 9$

$4 + 1 = 5$

| | | |
|---|---|---|
| $4 + 2 =$ | | $3 + 5 =$ | |
| $2 + 4 =$ | | $4 + 3 =$ | |
| $1 + 4 =$ | | $6 + 0 =$ | |
| $5 + 4 =$ | | $9 + 1 =$ | |
| $0 + 3 =$ | | $4 + 4 =$ | |
| $3 + 2 =$ | | $2 + 5 =$ | |
| $2 + 7 =$ | | $8 + 2 =$ | |

## Write the missing numerals.

| 3 | 4 | | 6 |

| 5 | | | 7 | 8 |

| 1 | | 3 | 4 |

| 7 | 8 | | 10 |

| Strand | Number |
| Strand Unit | Analysis of number |

Objectives   Combine two numbers, totals to 10.

$2 + 2 + 2 = 6$

☐ + ☐ + ☐ = ☐

☐ + ☐ + ☐ = ☐

☐ + ☐ + ☐ = ☐

☐ + ☐ + ☐ = ☐

## Add first, then colour. Use the colour key.

| Total | Colour |
|-------|--------|
| 2 | purple |
| 3 | red |
| 4 | green |
| 5 | orange |
| 6 | blue |
| 7 | yellow |

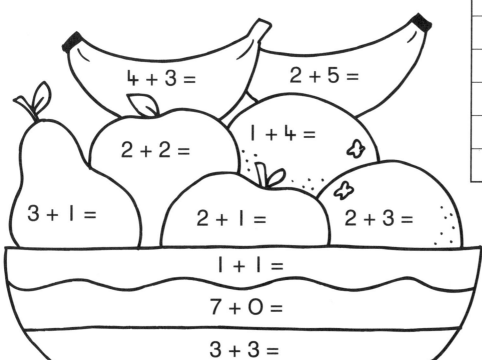

$4 + 3 =$

$2 + 5 =$

$2 + 2 =$

$1 + 4 =$

$3 + 1 =$

$2 + 1 =$

$2 + 3 =$

$1 + 1 =$

$7 + 0 =$

$3 + 3 =$

**Strand** Number
**Strand Unit** Analysis of number
Objectives  Combine three sets of objects totals to 10.
121

# Colour

**Colour the container that holds the least, red.**
**Colour the container that holds the most, blue.**

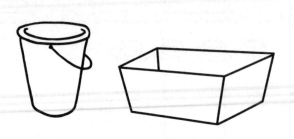

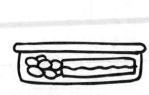

| Strand | Measures | Objectives | Compare and order containers according to |
|---|---|---|---|
| Strand Unit | Capacity | | capacity. |

**How many cups fill each object?**

count

my estimate [ ] amount [ ]

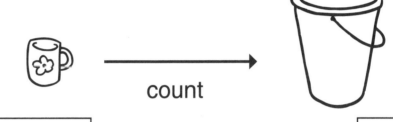
count

my estimate [ ] amount [ ]

count

my estimate [ ] amount [ ]

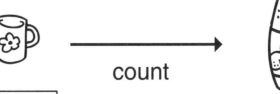
count

my estimate [ ] amount [ ]

# The Jungle

1. Draw **8** 🍌 on the big tree 🌴.

2. Finish the pattern on the 🐊.

3. Fill in the missing numbers on the 🐛.

4. Draw **2** more 🐟. Draw **4** spots on each 🐟.

5. Draw **2** tall 🌼 and **1** small 🌼 under the big tree.

| Strand | Number |
| --- | --- |
| Strand Unit | Counting |

Objectives — Counting sets of objects totals to 8.

## Colour the correct amount of boxes.

| | | | | | | | | |
|---|---|---|---|---|---|---|---|---|
| 🍌 | | | | | | | | |
| 🐛 | | | | | | | | |
| 🐟 | | | | | | | | |
| 🌸 | | | | | | | | |

# Lift

**Lift each pair of objects to find out which one is heavier.**
**Colour the heavy one red. Colour the light one green.**

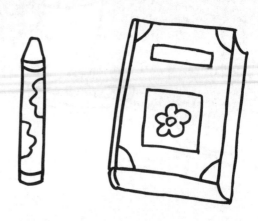

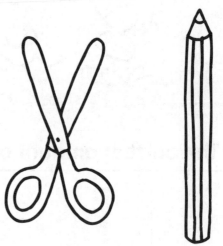

my Painting

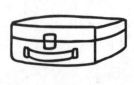

| Strand | Measures |
| --- | --- |
| Strand Unit | Weight |

Objectives: Compare the weight of objects that differ in size and shape by handling.

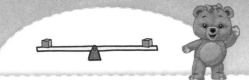
**Balance with cubes. Record.**

my estimate

cubes

How many cubes balance a ⬜ block?

my estimate

cubes

How many cubes balance a ▱ rubber?

my estimate

cubes

How many cubes balance a ✏ pencil?

my estimate

cubes

How many cubes balance a ▬ ruler?

The _____ is the **heaviest**.

The _____ is the **lightest**.

**Strand** Measures

**Strand Unit** Weight

Objectives

Estimate and weigh in non-standard units, check using balance.

127

# Add

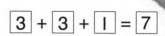
**Add. Use cubes or bears to help you.**

| | | | | |
|---|---|---|---|---|
| 3 | + 3 | + 1 | = | |
| 2 | + 4 | + 3 | = | |
| 5 | + 2 | + 1 | = | |
| 6 | + 2 | + 2 | = | |
| 7 | + 1 | + 0 | = | |

**Add first, then colour. Use the colour key.**

| Total | Colour |
|-------|--------|
| 7 | yellow |
| 8 | blue |
| 9 | green |
| 10 | red |

1 + 0 + 8 =

5 + 2 + 3 =

1 + 2 + 4 =

2 + 5 + 1 =

1 + 9 + 0 =

4 + 3 + 1 =

5 + 2 + 2 =

3 + 3 + 4 =

0 + 1 + 7 =

6 + 2 + 2 =

3 + 2 + 4 =

3 + 6 + 1 =

2 + 2 + 4 =

1 + 2 + 5 =

4 + 2 + 1 =

1 + 2 + 4 =

5 + 2 + 2 =

| Strand | Number | |
|--------|--------|---|
| Strand Unit | Analysis of number | Combine three numbers totals to 10. |

Objectives

128